Numbers with
The Gingerbread Man

Written by Janet Allison Brown
Illustrated by Samantha Chaffey

Colour
Library
Direct

A little old woman bakes her husband a Gingerbread Man. His eyes are made of chocolate buttons and his clothes are made of icing sugar.

The little old woman has baked 1 Gingerbread Man. Here he is, all alone, lying on the baking tray.

Copy him onto a piece of paper and then colour him in, using a nice rich brown for his eyes.

There are two ways of writing the number 1.

You can write it like this:

1

Or you can write it the simpler way, like this:

Practise writing the number 1 on a piece of paper.

Look at the picture opposite and answer these questions:

How many clocks are there?
How many ovens are there?
How many people are cooking?
How many Gingerbread Men has the little old woman baked?

Did you get the same answer for each question?
Was the answer 1? Well done!

But when the little old man came home, the
Gingerbread Man leaped off the plate and ran
away! "Come back!" cried the little old woman and
the little old man, and they started to run after him.

Why do you think the Gingerbread Man runs away? That's right – because he doesn't want to be eaten!

There are 2 people chasing the Gingerbread Man: the little old woman and the little old man.

The number 2 looks a little bit like a bird or a duck, with a beak.

How many things do you have 2 of?

You have 2 eyes and 2 ears.
You have 2 hands and 2 feet.
You have 2 arms and 2 legs.
You have 2 elbows and 2 knees!

2

A big black and white cow saw the Gingerbread Man
running across a field. "Yummy!" she thought. "I bet
I can run faster than a little old woman and a little
old man." And she started to run.

Now there are 3 people chasing the Gingerbread Man. Look at the picture opposite and count them.

1 little old woman + 1 little old man + 1 big black and white cow = 3.

(There is also a wily old fox spying on them from the trees, but we won't count him yet! Look out for him on every page from now on.)

Now try and answer these 3 questions:

1   How many black patches does the cow have?
2   How many trees are there growing in the field?
3   How many buttons does the Gingerbread Man have on his front?

A brown shire horse saw the Gingerbread Man running through a stable. "Yummy!" he thought. "I bet I can run faster than a little old woman, a little old man and a big black and white cow!" And he started to run.

Now there are 4 people chasing the Gingerbread Man! Practise writing the number 4 on a piece of paper. Then answer these questions:

How many horses are there in this picture?

If 2 horses go into the field, how many horses are left in the stable?
If 1 horse stays in the field, and 1 horse comes back to the stable, how many horses are in the stable now?

When you have the answers, try writing them down on a piece of paper.

How many legs does the cow have? How many legs does the horse have? Can you think of any other animals that have 4 legs?
Here are some pictures to help you get started:

A red-faced farmer saw the Gingerbread Man running through his farmyard. "Yummy!" he thought. "I bet I can run faster than a little old woman, a little old man, a cow and a brown shire horse!" And he started to run.

Now there are 5 people chasing the Gingerbread Man – count them!

The Gingerbread Man does not have any fingers and toes, but you do.
How many fingers do you have on your right hand? And how many fingers do you have on your left hand?
How many toes do you have on your right foot? And how many toes do you have on your left foot?

Here are 5 activities that all involve the number 5:

1. Name 5 of your favourite friends.

2. List 5 of your favourite dinners.

3. Go outside and collect 5 stones.
   Lay them on the table according to their size, smallest first.

4. On a piece of paper, write the number 5 five times.

5. Try to think of a word that rhymes with five.
                    Here's a clue:

A curly-haired schoolboy saw the Gingerbread Man running across the schoolyard. "Yummy!" he thought. "I bet I can run faster than a little old woman, a little old man, a cow, a horse and a red-faced farmer!" And he started to run.

Now there are 6 people chasing the Gingerbread Man – and all of them want to eat him!

Look at the row of numbers below. How many number 6s are there?

Now look at the picture below. There are 6 number 6s hiding in the picture – can you spot them?

A girl in pink ribbons saw the Gingerbread Man running across the street. "Yummy!" she thought. "I bet I can run faster than a little old woman, a little old man, a cow, a horse, a farmer and a curly-haired schoolboy!" And she started to run.

Now there are 7 people chasing the Gingerbread Man.
That's a lot of people. Let's take a look at the number 7:

Take 1 Gingerbread Man

add another to get 2

add another to get 3

add another to get 4

add another to get 5

add another to get 6

add another and then you'll have 7

So far the Gingerbread Man has been in 7 locations.
Can you name each of these locations?

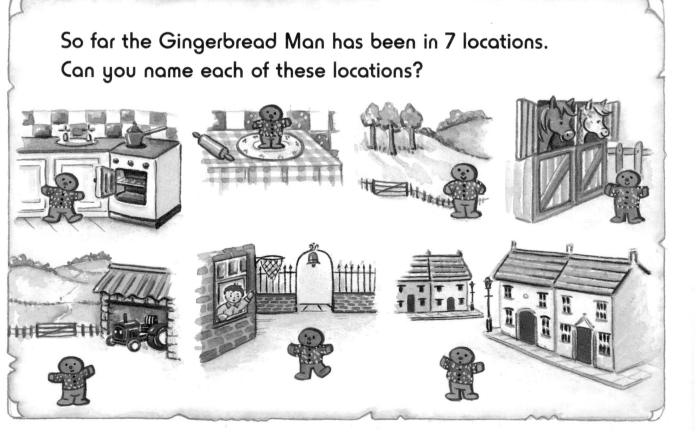

A hungry big dog saw the Gingerbread Man running across the street. "Yummy!" he thought. "I bet I can run faster than a little old woman, a little old man, a cow, a horse, a farmer, a schoolboy and a girl in pink ribbons!" And he started to run.

Now there are 8 people chasing the Gingerbread Man.
A good way of writing the number 8 is to draw two
small circles, one on top of the other.
Practise writing the number 8 on a piece of paper.

Look at the picture opposite. How many of those chasing the
Gingerbread Man are humans, and how many are animals?

5 humans

3 animals

plus 1 Gingerbread Man!

A proud white swan saw the Gingerbread Man running towards the river. "Yummy!" she thought. "I bet I can run faster than a little old woman, a little old man, a cow, a horse, a farmer, a schoolboy, a girl and a hungry big dog!" And she started to run.

Now there are 9 people chasing the Gingerbread Man. Try and remember each person, from the beginning, starting with the little old woman. For each person you count, hold up one finger. By the time you have finished, you should be holding up all but one of your fingers!

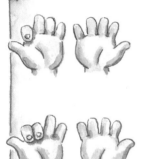

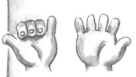

Now you can count from 1 to 9. But did you know you can also count *backwards* from 9 to 1? Yes you can! Do it this way: hold up 9 fingers. Now put down 1 finger and count how many fingers are left standing. The answer is 8. Now put down 1 finger and count how many fingers are left standing. The answer is 7. Keep going, and before you know it you will have counted backwards from 9 to 1. Well done!

Everybody in this story thinks that they can run faster than everybody else, but the Gingerbread Man runs the fastest of all. All the time he is being chased, the Gingerbread Man sings this little song:
"Run, run as fast as you can
You can't catch me, I'm the Gingerbread Man!"

At the river everyone came to a halt. "Where's my Gingerbread Man?" they all cried. They looked left and they looked right. They looked up and they looked down. And all they could see was a wily old fox licking his lips!